A beacon brazier, or cresset, at Goonhilly Future World visitor centre. ALAN KITTRIDGE

The beacon chain between Falmouth and Plymouth to warn of the sighting of the Spanish Armada

Cornish communications, as with the rest of Britain, were by word of mouth or pen and ink, carried by runners or riders on horseback. Any communication to another country had to go by sea. Speed is of the essence in communication but prior to electricity the only other option was by visual means. There is evidence to suggest that a chain of beacon fires extending westwards across Britain as far as Carn Brea (SW 386281) near Lands End has been in use since prehistoric times. Roman beacon stations possibly existed at High Cliff and Morwenstow. It is confusing that there are two beacon sites in Cornwall named Carn Brea, the other being at SW 685405 just to the south of Redruth.

A well-documented chain of beacons from Falmouth to Plymouth alerted the Navy of the Spanish Armada on 30 July 1588. Each beacon consisted of an iron brazier mounted on a pole to increase its visibility. The braziers were pre-loaded with a mixture of straw and pitch. It is said that, even when wet, such a mixture will light to a visible flame in about one minute. Thus the warning in Plymouth would be received in 10-20 minutes depending upon the vigilance of the observers. A chain of six beacons connected Falmouth to Plymouth. Obviously it must be possible for one beacon to be visible to the next and therefore they were on high vantage points. It would have taken a messenger on horseback about six hours

The church tower at Paul, near Mousehole, was the location for a beacon JOHN MOYLE

SOME SITES OF FIRE BEACONS

Carn Brea	SW 386281
Carn Galver	SW 425365
Fire Beacon Point (near Boscastle)	SX 105925
St Agnes Beacon	SW 705505
St Cleer	SX 247681

As many as 20 other probable fire-beacon sites in Cornwall were located on areas of high ground which bear the name 'Beacon'.

NELSON AND TRAFALGAR

Although by 1805 there was an efficient shutter telegraph service between Portsmouth and the Admiralty in London, Vice Admiral Collingwood chose to send the news of the victory at Trafalgar and Nelson's death *via* Falmouth and then by hand on to London. Collingwood took over command of the Fleet on the death of Nelson on 21 October. He dispatched Lt Lapenotière in command of the schooner *HMS Pickle*. *HMS Pickle* had dumped four canons overboard to increase her speed and she made her first landfall at the Cornish port of Falmouth on 4 November. He then proceeded to London by post-chaise and reported to the Admiralty 38 hours later – a journey which normally took a week.

HMS **Pickle**

Maker church tower, near Plymouth, was the site of an Admiralty semaphore. ALAN KITTRIDGE

to ride the 60 miles between Falmouth and Plymouth.

Sometimes it is only local history which locates beacon sites. An example is the documented use of the Parish Church Tower at Paul (SW 464270) just inland from Mousehole.

The traditional beacon sites are still used, if only for moments of national celebration, as during the Queen's Jubilee year of 1977, and again to signal the marriage of Prince Charles to Lady Diana Spencer in 1981.

Beacons of fire could only send notification of a single piece of information already expected by the recipient. More complex techniques were required to send messages. Many of these methods were first developed for use at sea.

Both 'telegraph' and 'semaphore' are derived from ancient Greek. Telegraph literally means 'to write at a distance' and semaphore 'to bear a sign'. Their modern usage was coined by two Frenchmen: Télégraphe by Claude Chappe in 1793 and Sémaphore (meaning signalling by flags) from ship to shore by Depillon in 1801. Surprisingly, the more complex shutter telegraph for long distance communication was developed in England before the semaphore system. A documented site of an Admiralty semaphore is on the church tower at Maker.

One source implies a line of shutter telegraphs extending

from west of Falmouth to London but there is no evidence that shutter telegraphs were used west of Plymouth. In Cornwall only the semaphore method was used. The routes of optical telegraphs, particularly in the home counties, can be traced on large scale maps by the occurrence of names such as 'Telegraph House' and 'Telegraph Hill'. The Isles of Scilly had no form of communication with the mainland other than by sea until the Telegraph tower was built in 1814. A mechanical semaphore was installed atop the tower. Signalling was slow and liable to interruption by bad weather but the islands were to wait for over half a century for anything better, and even then they did not get exactly what they had expected.

Today, the probable sites of beacons and semaphore telegraphs are used for microwave communications which are also 'line-of-sight' technology but fortunately do not rely on good weather and daylight.

Admiralty Semaphore now in use.

No. of Signal by 1 and 2 Arms.	Signification.	No. of Signal by 1 and 2 Arms.	Signification.	No. of Signal by 1 and 2 Arms.	Signification.
1	1	15	G	43	X
2	2	16	H	44	Y
3	3	21	I	45	Z
4	4	22	K	46	
5	5	23	L	51	
6	6	24	M	52	
1	A	25	N	53	
2	B	26	O	54	
3	C	31	P	55	
4	D	32	Qu	56	
5	E	33	R	61	
6	F	34	S	62	
11	7	35	T	63	
12	8	36	U	64	
13	9	41	V	65	
14	0	42	W	66	

In all—48 separate and distinct signals; being the whole which the two arms are capable of making, as under; in which the two arms actually exhibited (in black lines) represent the number 16 or H, according to the table or *key*, as above arranged.

We have here, in addition to the alphabet and the numeral digits, 13 signs over, applicable to the names of stations, preparative, finish, stop-signals, &c.

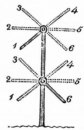

Admiralty Semaphore c1825

Semaphore code COURTESY BARRIE KENT

FLAGS AND THE ROYAL NAVY

The Royal Navy had used combinations of static signal flags from about 1338. Various code books of flag combinations were published and regularly updated. Indeed, message flags are still used by today's navies but more for ceremonial than operational use.

During the Napoleonic Wars code flags were used to signal between ships and ship-to-shore. Shore stations in Cornwall were either fixed or mobile.

Code books contain combinations of 2 or 3 flags to signify common messages. For messages which were not in the codebooks 'flag-wagging' or semaphore, using a flag held in each hand, was a common method of signalling in daylight by navies until after the second World War. Nowadays, apart from a few specific safety signal flags (eg 'pilot on board', 'healthy ship' etc) all maritime signalling is by radio.

The Telegraph tower, Isles of Scilly
NEVILLE NEWNHAM

SEMAPHORE SIGNAL STATIONS IN CORNWALL	
Maker Heights	SX 446517
Penheale	SX 265885
Talland	SX 225515
Dodman Point	SX 001393
St Anthony Head	SW 847312
Manacles Point	SW 810393
Black Head	SX 039479
Lizard Point	SW 695115
Tater Du	SW 440230
St Levan's Point	SW 382223
Carn Brea	SW 386281
Gribbin Head	SX 097497
Tregonning Hill	SW 602297
Telegraph Tower (Scilly)	SV 9112

The distance over which semaphore could be used was enhanced by improvements in telescopes but also by using large mechanically operated signal arms. Indeed, mechanical semaphore arms mounted on the top of Telegraph Tower (165 feet above sea level) on St Mary's, Isles of Scilly in 1814, were the only rapid means of communication with the mainland until a submarine telegraph cable was laid.

LIZARD SIGNAL STATION

After ships had been at sea for long periods there was anxiety both for those on land and those on the ships to contact each other. G. C. Fox and Company, ship owners and agents, built an observation and signalling station on the cliff at Bass Point on the eastern edge of Housel Bay in April 1872. There was a signal mast on the flat roof and in fine weather ships were able to communicate with the station by flags.

It was not unknown for ships to come to grief on the rocks of the Lizard because they had ventured too close so as to read the flag messages. Just this happened to a beautiful four-masted barque, the *Queen Elizabeth* as late as 1913.

Lloyds signal station flying a hoist requesting ships to identify themselves. ALAN KITTRIDGE COLLECTION

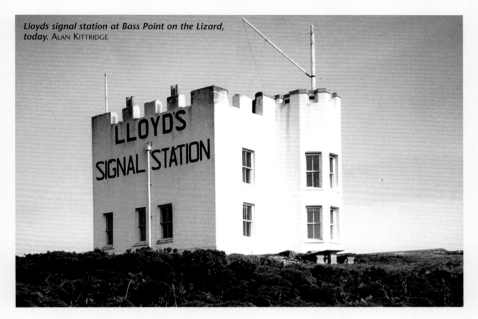

Lloyds signal station at Bass Point on the Lizard, today. ALAN KITTRIDGE

At night time, coloured lights and various pyrotechnics were used. It was not until June 1872 that a reliable telegraph cable was laid to Falmouth to connect with the newly laid submarine cable from Bass Point to Bilbao. The Lizard Signal Station was then also connected to Falmouth where many shipping companies had offices. By that time telegraph lines covered the country and therefore news of safe arrival would reach the major conurbations within a few minutes.

A rival shipping company, William Broad & Sons, also set-up a station adjacent to Fox's Station and there was much acrimony for several years before they decided to join forces and use Fox's building. Broad's wooden shack has long since disappeared. Lloyds took over the operation of the Signal Station in 1883 and it was operated by them until 1951 when HM Coastguard Service continued to observe shipping. In 1994 the Lizard Signal Station was handed over to the National Trust who renovated it and it is leased out by them as a private residence.

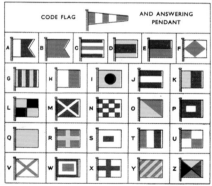

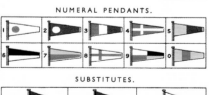

The international code of signals

When fish were sighted by huer, hevva was made by calling through the trumpet

Weigh anchor

Go to Eastward

Go out to Sea

Wind away warp, stop by dropping left hand

See or Stand Quiet

'Get all ready' shouted through trumpet

'Cowl Rooz' or Cast net

Go to East

Go right Eastward

Steady

Go to Westward

Come together

Down anchor OR cancell all previous signals when there are no fish

THE METHOD OF SIGNALLING WITH BUSHES USED IN PILCHARD SEINE FISHERY

COURTESY KEITH HARRIS

Newquay huers' hut COURTESY SIMON AT WWW.THEHIDAWAY.CO.UK

HEVVA!

A method of maritime communication in Cornwall was the shout 'Hevva' from high coastal vantage points by men known as huers to direct fishing boats to shoals of pilchards which were seen as a stain of red, purple and silver in the water. The huer used battens, paddles or gorse brush for this form of semaphore. Because he was sited at a high exposed spot, the huer was usually provided with a hut for protection from the elements. The known sites of huer's huts are at Towan Head near Newquay and the ruins of a huer's hut at Cribba Head (SW403224) near Penberth.

NEWQUAY HUERS' HUT

The 'hut' at Newquay overlooks Towan Beach and is a substantial building which may have been built originally as hermitage in the 14th century. The hermit was entrusted with lighting beacon fires to guide ships in the days before lighthouses.

The Royal Mail is so named because its original use was solely for the delivery of messages for the sovereign. It developed to carry mail for the general population when the sovereign realised it would make a great source of income.

Even in the early days of mail, all rivers and streams were crossable over good quality bridges whilst the roads between were atrocious. The reason for this was that the during the Tudor period Lords of the Manor were instructed by the Crown to build and maintain the bridges on their lands whilst the roads were the responsibility of the parish. The mails were mainly carried by horse back. The Mail Coach, a massive vehicle hauled by six horses, came into use in 1784 but was more impressive than useful because of its large size. The first Mail Coach came to Cornwall in 1799.

With the constant fear of invasion by Spain, the Post road to the West Country and especially to Cornwall became of vital importance. Even after the Armada was defeated in 1588, the West Country ports remained at a high state of alert for many years. The main route to Cornwall from London was *via* Exeter to Plymouth. The mails were then carried by ferry across the Tamar estuary to Torpoint and then on *via* St Austell and Truro to Falmouth. Thomas Randolph, Master of the 'Royal Mails', organised a system of 'foot posts' as part of the Armada warning system. He ordered that every parish along the coast must have someone living near the parish church be appointed as a foot postman. This man received a fee of six pence per week and had to be ready to run to the nearest Post Town (town with a sorting office that has to be named as part of any address in the UK) with the news that the enemy galleons had been sighted. This was in parallel to the chain of beacons. By 1650 Penzance had become a Post Town.

After the Armada emergency was over the foot postmen remained as a service for the villages which had previously been virtually cut-off from anything but haphazard information. There is a striking parallel in the way extra telephone lines were put down during 1940 for air raid and invasion warning.

THE PACKET SERVICE 1688-1850

For almost two hundred years Falmouth was the centre of the packet ship fleet. In 1688 the Post Office recognised Falmouth as being the main port for overseas mail. In its official report it recorded:

The extreme westerly position of Falmouth harbour gives it an advantage which is rendered obvious by a single glance at a map. From no other harbour in this country can an outward-bound vessel clear the land so quickly; no other so soon reached by one homeward bound and running for shelter. On the darkest nights and in dense fog, ships unacquainted with the harbour may enter it safely, so easy is it of access; and sailing vessels can leave it in any wind, save one blowing strongly from the east or south-east. It is, in fact, the safest anchorage in the country, protected from the full strength of the Atlantic rollers and abounding in sheltered creeks where vessels may be in practical immunity from the worst of the storms.

Before 1688, important mails, usually emanating from London, were carried by the first ship available whose destination was suitable. In 1688 the Post Office chartered two vessels from a local man named Daniel Gwin. The vessels were allowed to carry passengers or cargo to improve their financial viability and the PO also provided the crews. The vessels were known as packets, the word being derived from pacquet, the leather bag in which the sovereign's messengers carried royal mail. By 1702 the service had grown dramatically under the lead of Edward Dummer.

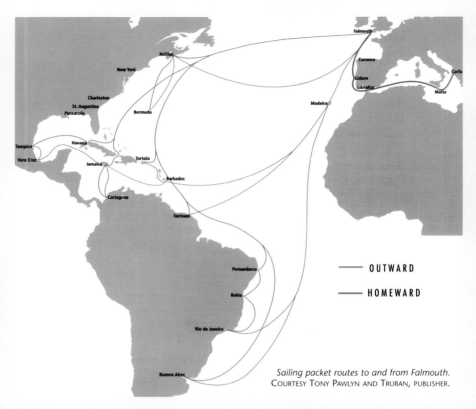

Sailing packet routes to and from Falmouth.
COURTESY TONY PAWLYN AND TRURAN, PUBLISHER.

The high seas were generally lawless in those days. The packet ships were armed but mainly had to rely upon speed and agility to escape privateers and pirates, both French and American. They were lightly armed compared with their opponents and had orders to avoid engagement and run whenever possible. If there was the slightest chance of capture, the mails were to be thrown overboard. Unfortunately the packet ships were very tempting to their attackers as they would be carrying bullion as well as mail. There are many heroic tales of the packet crews attempting to get the mail to its destination.

King Charles II forbade the carrying of 'ventures' (goods) aboard packet vessels but the packet captains took little notice of the ruling. These goods were the main source of income to the packet crews. The situation came to a head in 1810 when the Post Office enforced this ruling thereby leading to a 'mutiny' by the packet crews. The Royal Navy forced the Packet Fleet to move to Plymouth. The mutiny quickly collapsed as the Packet Service was the main reason for the prosperity of Falmouth at the time.

By 1830 the advent of the steamer heralded the demise of the Packet Service. In 1842, the Peninsular & Oriental Steam Navigation Company began to introduce big, fast steamships on mail routes and Samuel Cunard won the contract for the North American mail. The sailing ships were phased out and by 1852 the role of Falmouth as Britain's chief packet port came to an end.

It may come as a surprise that the first practical use of electricity was for communication. Early electrical telegraphy was invented long before electricity was used for lighting or motive power. Prior to telegraphy, electricity was just a scientific curiosity and even a magical phenomenon relegated to stage performances.

Morse inker. JOHN MOYLE

'Practical' as opposed to 'experimental' electrical telegraphy in Britain began in 1837 with the Wheatstone and Cooke 5-needle telegraph system which used 5 wires. The 5 wires were electrically insulated by individually gluing them with pitch in grooves cut in wood; this meant that the 'cables' were expensive and only short distances were covered.

Telegraph technology was simplified and therefore became more economical with the invention of Morse code by Samuel Morse in 1832. Using this simple code intelligence could be transmitted rapidly using only a single wire and an 'earth return' (using the electrical conductivity of the terra firma or sea water as the second conductor to complete a circuit). His original 'American' code was simplified to an International version which is still in use by radio amateurs although its professional use ceased in 1999.

Telegraphy did not reach Cornwall until 1860. By this time the well-known Morse key and Morse-inker and 'sounder' were in common use; only a single wire conductor was necessary as the earth was used to complete the circuit. Surprisingly, the complicated Morse-inker was used long before the sounder. It was only when the telegraphists of the time realised that they were able to decode the clicking sounds made by the inker that this simpler, cheaper and more reliable method became the norm. The sounder also made the skill of the telegrapher much sought after.

By 1867 Truro and Penzance were connected by land-line to all the other major centres in Britain. Commonly, telegraph wires were alongside railways which provided a continuous track of land across the country. Air was the main insulator used between telegraph stations. Iron and (later) copper wires were suspended between poles or buildings using glass or porcelain insulators. Indoors, cotton or silk was wound around the conductors to

Morse sounder. JOHN MOYLE

International Morse Code

A	• —	T	—
B	— • • •	U	• • —
C	— • — •	V	• • • —
D	— • •	W	• — —
E	•	X	— • • —
F	• • — •	Y	— • — —
G	— — •	Z	— — • •
H	• • • •		
I	• •	1	• — — — —
J	• — — —	2	• • — — —
K	— • —	3	• • • — —
L	• — • •	4	• • • • —
M	— —	5	• • • • •
N	— •	6	— • • • •
O	— — —	7	— — • • •
P	• — — •	8	— — — • •
Q	— — • —	9	— — — — •
R	• — •	0	— — — — —
S	• • •		

insulate them; India rubber was also later used. However, telegraphy was limited to use on land for want of a suitable insulating material for use under water. Rubber was found to be unsuitable for long distance submarine cables, one reason being that rubber slowly absorbs sea water. Submarine cables were not successful until a new insulating material called gutta percha was discovered. Gutta percha is a resin that comes from the *Isonandra Gutta* tree which grows in a limited area of the Far East. It has properties not dissimilar to rubber: above 60 degrees Celsius it becomes mouldable; at room temperature it becomes hard. It also has very good electrical insulating properties which actually improve at the low temperature and high pressure encountered at great

Gutta percha tree

depths. The first under-sea telegraph cables from Britain were from Dover to France. The first two attempts to lay a trans-Atlantic telegraph cable by *HMS Agamemnon* in 1857 and 1858 were expensive failures. A successful cable was laid in 1865 by Brunel's *Great Eastern* between Valentia in Ireland and Newfoundland. This was extended at each end to join New York to London.

The conductor was copper wire; this was surrounded by gutta percha. Next was a layer of thin brass tape the purpose of which was not to conduct electricity but to stop marine creatures from boring their way through the gutta percha! Protection from mechanical wear was provided by layers of hemp soaked in Chatterton's compound (a mixture of three parts gutta percha, one part resin, one part Stockholm pitch) and finally by steel wires wound around the outside.

Britain in the late 19th century had many dominions and it was considered important that the instant communication provided by telegraphy should connect

Section of nineteenth century submarine cable

London with the Empire. Although speed of communication had vast advantages, there were some disadvantages as well. Diplomats became less skilled as it was so easy for them to defer problems to London. Commanders on the field of battle had to continuously report to their masters in London who in return continuously interfered with the conduct of battle. Cornwall was the ideal starting point for this huge network.

PORTHCURNO

In 1870 Porthcurno began its life as an important centre of international communications. It was in this year that a chain of telegraph cables linking Britain with India was completed. Porthcurno

LANDING THE CABLE AT PORTHCURNEW BAY.

Landing Porthcurno's first cable in 1870

was chosen as the landing point for the British end of this cable link. The company that laid the cable into Porthcurno was the Falmouth, Gibraltar and Malta Telegraph Company, founded by John Pender in 1869 and one of four companies established to lay the cables in the 'chain' linking Britain and India. The name of the company indicates that the cable was to land at Falmouth and this was indeed the original intention. However, late in the planning, it was decided to land the cable at Porthcurno rather than Falmouth. This was because there was less risk of the cable being damaged by anchors and fishing equipment. Hence this remote Cornish cove became the site of Britain's first major Empire communications link in 1870. In 1872 the four small companies that had laid the Porthcurno to Bombay cable were merged to form the Eastern Telegraph Company. This company went on to develop a world-wide telegraph cable network and Porthcurno was its major station.

Porthcurno valley 1870

THE FALMOUTH, GIBRALTAR, AND MEDITERRANEAN TELEGRAPH.

THE CLIFFS AT PORTHCURNEW BAY, CORNWALL.

Porthcurno's telegraphic code name was 'PK'. At its height, Porthcurno was the world's largest cable station, with 14 telegraph cables in operation.

13

The signals from submarine cables were substantially weaker (1-5 thousandths of an ampere) than land-lines because of the extreme distances between stations and the lack of amplifiers. This was, after all, many years before the electronic (thermionic) valve (known as 'tube' in the US) had been invented. Two extremely sensitive devices namely the mirror galvanometer and the siphon galvanometer were developed by Professor William Thomson (later Lord Kelvin).

THE SIPHON RECORDER AND MIRROR GALVANOMETER

The simple galvanometer is a detector of electrical current. It relies upon the interaction between current and a permanent magnetic field but had limited sensitivity. Electronic amplification was more than 50 years away at a time when extreme sensitivity was required. In 1858 William Thomson, Professor of Physics at Glasgow University, increased the galvanometer's sensitivity by attaching a tiny mirror to the needle. An oil lamp was used to project a spot of light at the mirror which reflected it to a horizontal scale. Thus minute movement of the mirror was magnified and currents in the micro-ampere range could be detected in laboratory grade versions.

The Thomson Siphon Recorder was the first recording galvanometer which was sensitive enough to make a direct recording of signals from long-distance submarine cables. The siphon recorder may be considered the earliest ink-jet printer.

The mirror galvanometer required one operator to concentrate on the movement of the light spot and a second operator to transcribe the message. The siphon recorder only needed one operator to decode the message which was

In the siphon recorder the mirror is replaced by a capillary tube through which ink flows onto a moving paper tape ('slip'). The capillary tube does not actually come in contact with the paper as the friction would be to great for the small deflecting current. Ink is drawn from the tube to the paper by 'static' electricity.
JOHN MOYLE

safely recorded on the paper slip. Because this was before the days of electronic amplification, repeater stations were needed at least every 2,000 miles.

A mirror galvanometer with its cover removed. The minute deflection of the tiny mirror by a very small electric current is magnified by allowing it to reflect a narrow beam of light onto a 9 inch scale.
JOHN MOYLE

In 1869 a telegraph cable was laid linking Cornwall with the Scilly Isles. The cable entered the sea just west of Porthcurno at Zawn Reeth (SW 352238). Hoax and questionable integrity accompanied the cable to the Scillies. The *Fusilier* set off from Zawn Reeth with either insufficient cable or a poorly chosen route

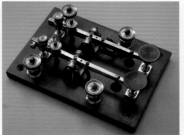

Double Cable Key for submarine cables. One key sent dots, the other dashes.
JOHN MOYLE

and the cable came to an end five miles before reaching St Mary's. Whilst the dignitaries and a band awaited the arrival of the cable, the captain deliberately snapped the cable and dragged the last mile or so of it into St Mary's. The electricians then pretended to the scientifically naive observers that all was well. The link was finally completed the following year but failed in 1877. When it was repaired it was diverted into Porthcurno.

A telegraph cable was laid from Porthcurno to Carcavellos in Portugal by the Falmouth, Gibraltar and Malta Telegraph Company in 1870. This linked up with other undersea cables which connected Britain with India. In 1872 a telegraph cable was laid from Vigo in Spain to Porthcurno. In that year, staff cottages were built in the valley.

The diagram on page 21 shows all the cables laid from Cornwall until the present day. However only the first section from Cornwall to the next station are listed. The majority of cables progressed far beyond the first section shown. For example, by 1876 there was connection from London to New Zealand *via* Porthcurno, Vigo (Spain), Lisbon

Porthcurno staff 1871. PK TRUST ARCHIVE

SPIES AT WIRELESS POINT

By 1902 Marconi's increasing successes with wireless telegraphy caused the cable companies to worry about the competition. The Eastern Telegraph Company engaged in some industrial espionage by setting up a receiving station at what is now known as Wireless Point above the Porthcurno valley. All that can be seen now is the base of the mast, which resembles a medieval instrument of torture.

(Portugal), Gibraltar, Malta, Alexandria, Suez, Bombay (Mumbai, India), Madras, Penang, Singapore, Djakarta (Indonesia), Banjoewangie (West Java), Darwin, Adelaide, Sydney, Cable Bay (New Zealand). At each Station, the message would be transcribed and re-transmitted as this was before automatic repeaters and regenerators.

The first connection from Porthcurno to North America was *via* Brest in France. In 1879 La Compagnie Francaise du Telegraphe laid a cable from Brest to Cape Breton Island and thence to Cape Cod. The following year the company laid a cable from Brest to Porthcurno, terminating half way between Porthcurno beach and Logan Rock, a surprising landfall as it was at a steep cliff. Connection from a cable hut at the top of the cliff continued by land line to the company's office in Penzance. In Cornwall the company was known as the PQ Company after one of its directors, Monsieur Pouyer-Quertier. In the

1930s the maintenance of the cable was taken over by the Eastern Telegraph Company at Porthcurno. The dilapidated cable hut was demolished and replaced by a stone pyramid (SW 391224) by the National Trust in the 1950s.

The trials and tribulations of living and working in such a remote place as Porthcurno were highlighted by the letters from the Superintendent at Porthcurno to the Company's Managing Director in London. 'We are in a very awkward fix being without a cook . . . it is very difficult to get any to come here at all. They won't leave Penzance as this place is too dull for them.'

The Great Blizzard in 1891 broke telegraph landlines linking Porthcurno with Penzance and bent the telegraph poles; staff volunteered to walk into Penzance with the telegrams. When they got there they sent a telegram back to say they had arrived safely but because the landline between Porthcurno and Penzance had been pulled down by the snow, this message was sent on a cable from Penzance *via* Malta, New York and Brest.

By the close of the nineteenth century, Porthcurno was well established in the world of telecommunications as an important working cable station. At this time, submarine telegraph cables were still the only means of long-distance telecommunication as radio was still in its experimental stages. In 1902 Marconi carried out radio experiments from his station at Poldhu on the Lizard and succeeded in sending a 'wireless' signal across the Atlantic.

During the Great War, the Royal Navy deliberately cut any undersea cables that connected Germany with her Allies. Increasing isolation then forced Berlin to use the only two remaining transatlantic cables: the Swedish one from Stockholm to Buenos Aires and the American State Department line which ran from Copenhagen. Both the Swedish proprietors and the US State Department neglected to inform Berlin that these two cables both went through the UK! Copies of all Berlin's telegrams *via* these cables were sent automatically to the Admiralty's Room 40 in London for decoding.

In 1921 the cable from Bilbao in Spain which had previously landed at the Lizard was diverted into Porthcurno. 1925 saw the introduction of automatic 'regeneration'. Regeneration was designed to enable telegraphic messages on long cable chains to be automatically received, 'cleaned up' and re-transmitted on to the next station, without the need for human intervention. By this time Marconi's radio telegraph network was highly successful and the profits of the Eastern Telegraph Company were falling. The Imperial Wireless and Cable Conference was held in London in 1928. The outcome was the merger of the Eastern Telegraph Company with the telegraph network of Marconi to form a new company, Imperial and International Communications Limited. The immediate effect of the merger at Porthcurno was the addition of two cables which were bought from the British Post Office. They were diverted from their original landing place at Mousehole; one was an old

Porthcurno to Harbour Grace, Canada cable 1874. JOHN MOYLE

cable which had been laid in 1874 and went to Harbour Grace in Newfoundland. The other had once been a German cable and went to Fayal in the Azores. This left Porthcurno with 14 working telegraph cables and made it undeniably the most important cable station on the British Empire's communications network. In 1934 the name of Imperial and International Communications Limited was changed to Cable & Wireless Limited.

SECOND WORLD WAR TUNNELS AT PORTHCURNO

The Second World War began in 1939. Underground tunnels were cut into the cliff behind the main building to house the telegraph station and protect it from attack. The tunnels were air conditioned and bomb-proof. All telegraph instruments were moved into the tunnels and the main building was camouflaged.

For further protection against attack from the sea, pipes were laid just below the surface of the sand across the bay. They were connected to a large tank of petrol half way up the cliff. If there was an amphibious attack the landing forces could be incinerated.

Instrument room in the tunnels 1944.
PK TRUST ARCHIVE

Porthcurno Telegraph Museum, ex Cable & Wireless Telegraph Engineering College. JOHN MOYLE

In 1947 Cable & Wireless was nationalised by the post-war Labour government. As a result, the British Post Office took over the UK assets of the company with the exception of Porthcurno. The training facilities at Porthcurno were expanded and the Cable & Wireless Telegraph Engineering College (for staff who were headed overseas) was officially opened. A new telegraph cable was laid to Harbour Grace in Newfoundland in 1952. This was the last major telegraph cable to be laid by Cable & Wireless due to the development of new telephone cables which took over from

Part of the working display inside the tunnels at the Porthcurno Telegraph Museum. JOHN MOYLE

the telegraph during the 1960s. In 1970 after exactly a century as a working cable station, the last telegraph circuit closed at Porthcurno, ending the village's life as a telegraph station. However, Cable & Wireless continued to expand its training facilities with students attending from all over the world. In 1993 the Cable & Wireless college at Porthcurno closed and four years later, on 28 March 1997, the Cable & Wireless Museum of Submarine Telegraphy opened.

An old telegraph cable exposed on Porthcurno beach. PK Trust Archive

The PK Trust, an independent educational charity, was set up in 1997 by Cable & Wireless plc to preserve the important historical buildings and collections at Porthcurno, the home of the British Empire's first international telecommunications network, 'the Victorian internet'. The Trust's two major activities are operation of the award-winning Porthcurno Telegraph Museum and the management of the Cable & Wireless historic archive of photographs, films and documents. By providing access to these unique, world-class historical resources, the PK Trust is developing Porthcurno's reputation as an important centre for the study of the history of communications. The staff and team of skilled volunteers, many of them retired Cable & Wireless engineers, who maintain and operate the historic equipment, provide talks and tours and give the museum its great atmosphere.

Cable hut just above high-water level on Porthcurno Beach; termination of cables to Gibraltar, Lisbon, Vigo (Spain), Madeira, Fayal (Azores), Newfoundland, Valentia (Ireland), Bilbao. PK Trust archive

The escape stairway inside the wartime tunnels at Porthcurno Telegraph Museum. PK TRUST ARCHIVE

The main building houses displays of the history of submarine telegraphy from geographical, economic and social points of view. The tunnels contain displays and demonstrations of the technology from the first days of cable telegraphy through to the fibre optic cables of today.

Porthcurno Telegraph Museum. JOHN MOYLE

Cable Hut, Porthcurno beach. JOHN MOYLE

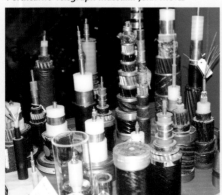

THE CABLES OF CORNWALL TODAY

The late 20th century saw the peak in the use of satellites for long distance communication and although this technology will continue to be used in the future, under-sea cables are making a resurgence. This is due to the vast cost of satellite technology compared with that of laying fibre-optic rather than electric cables. Optical fibres carrying signals in the form of coded pulses of light do not have the problems associated with electrical insulation from sea water. When constructed from modern materials they are simpler, lighter and require less maintenance. Many more simultaneous 'circuits' can be carried by optical cables than their electrical counterparts and so there has been a resurgence in cable laying, especially over relatively short distances.

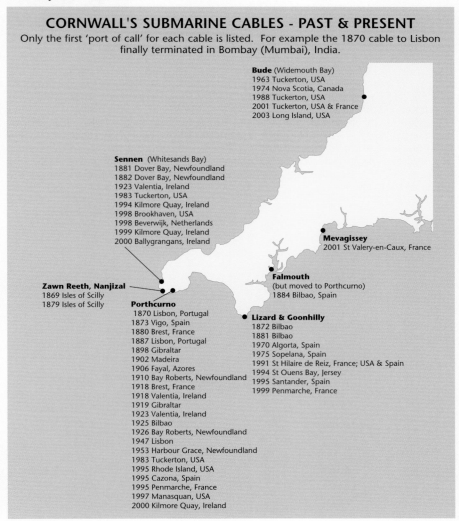

CORNWALL'S SUBMARINE CABLES - PAST & PRESENT

Only the first 'port of call' for each cable is listed. For example the 1870 cable to Lisbon finally terminated in Bombay (Mumbai), India.

Bude (Widemouth Bay)
1963 Tuckerton, USA
1974 Nova Scotia, Canada
1988 Tuckerton, USA
2001 Tuckerton, USA & France
2003 Long Island, USA

Sennen (Whitesands Bay)
1881 Dover Bay, Newfoundland
1882 Dover Bay, Newfoundland
1923 Valentia, Ireland
1983 Tuckerton, USA
1994 Kilmore Quay, Ireland
1998 Brookhaven, USA
1998 Beverwijk, Netherlands
1999 Kilmore Quay, Ireland
2000 Ballygrangans, Ireland

Mevagissey
2001 St Valery-en-Caux, France

Zawn Reeth, Nanjizal
1869 Isles of Scilly
1879 Isles of Scilly

Falmouth
(but moved to Porthcurno)
1884 Bilbao, Spain

Porthcurno
1870 Lisbon, Portugal
1873 Vigo, Spain
1880 Brest, France
1887 Lisbon, Portugal
1898 Gibraltar
1902 Madeira
1906 Fayal, Azores
1910 Bay Roberts, Newfoundland
1918 Brest, France
1918 Valentia, Ireland
1919 Gibraltar
1923 Valentia, Ireland
1925 Bilbao
1926 Bay Roberts, Newfoundland
1947 Lisbon
1953 Harbour Grace, Newfoundland
1983 Tuckerton, USA
1995 Rhode Island, USA
1995 Cazona, Spain
1995 Penmarche, France
1997 Manasquan, USA
2000 Kilmore Quay, Ireland

Lizard & Goonhilly
1872 Bilbao
1881 Bilbao
1970 Algorta, Spain
1975 Sopelana, Spain
1991 St Hilaire de Reiz, France; USA & Spain
1994 St Ouens Bay, Jersey
1995 Santander, Spain
1999 Penmarche, France

MARCONI AND WIRELESS

Marconi led the field in the development of practical working systems of telecommunication by wireless but he must not be considered the sole inventor of radio, or wireless as it was originally called. A long line of theorists and inventors came before: Michael Faraday (1791-1867); Professor James Clerk Maxwell (1831-1879); Heinrich Hertz (1857-1894) in Germany; Oliver Lodge (1851-1940) in London; and Edouard Branley (1844-1874) in France; between them invented and developed the major instruments but did not see how they could be put together to make a system of 'wireless' communication. A scientific visionary, William Crookes (1832-1919) in England, speculated upon communication without wires. Aleksander Popov (1859-1906) in Russia; Nikola Tesla (1856-1943) in the USA; Captain Henry Jackson RN (1855-1929) in England; and Marconi (1874 1937) in Italy; simultaneously began investigating the possibility of wireless telegraphy but it was Marconi initially in Italy and then in England who developed the first working system.

Guglielmo Marconi
MUSEUM OF SCIENCE, OXFORD.

Guglielmo Marchese Marconi, was born in Italy of an Italian father and an Irish mother. By 1895 he had successfully transmitted Morse code over a distance of two miles but he was unable to interest the Italian government, so he moved to England in 1896. He was gifted with technical ability, business acumen and an ability to manage the Press. Because of these skills he was able to develop Wireless telegraphy ahead of his rivals.

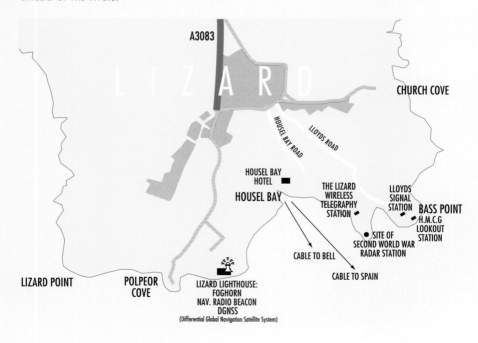

MARCONI & THE LIZARD

Why the Lizard? So far away from London and also Chelmsford where the Marconi factory was and still is. Marconi's challenge was to communicate with the New World and geographically Cornwall provided the shortest pathway for radio signals to North America. Lizard Point is the most southerly part of the UK. Its importance in the history of communications also lies in the fact that for the majority of shipping visiting the south of England the Lizard was the first sight of land, after many months at sea in the case of sailing ships from the Americas. The Lizard Peninsula is probably the most important communications heritage site in the whole of the UK. In an area of a few square miles there are the Lloyds Signal Station, the Lizard Lighthouse, the Lizard Wireless Station, the Housel Bay Hotel (where Marconi stayed whilst at the Lizard), Poldhu and Goonhilly. Poldhu has the monument on the site of the Poldhu Wireless Station from which Marconi made the first trans-Atlantic radio contact. Goonhilly was a major earth station for satellite communication.

Marconi set up the Lizard station in 1901 within a few miles of Poldhu for three reasons. He needed a local station for checking Poldhu transmissions there was a land-line telegraph between them. Another reason for the close proximity was to test the efficacy of 'syntonic' (that is tuned) circuits in the vicinity of a powerful transmitter. Additionally Lizard Radio was to be the most south-westerly station for ship-to-shore communication

The Housel Bay Hotel became Marconi's second home whilst he worked at the Lizard. JOHN MOYLE

SYNTONY

The earliest successful wireless transmissions were unknown, un-tuned, random, covering a wide frequency range. This caused enormous problems as only one pair of stations could communicate at any one time. In 1900 Marconi developed tuned or 'syntonic' transmitters and receivers. The chosen frequencies were known as 'tunes'. The principles of syntony were published by Professor Oliver Lodge in 1897 but the practical techniques were patented by Marconi in 1901 in his most famous British Patent No 7777, known as the 'Four Sevens' patent which caused considerable acrimony between Lodge and Marconi.

The Lizard Wireless Station with the Lloyds signal station in the background. ALAN KITTRIDGE

LIZARD WIRELESS STATION

The original wooden building of the Lizard Wireless Station still stands in its exposed position which is testament to the construction work of 1900. Marconi built it to conduct experiments in long distance wireless, which began in January 1901 with his record-breaking transmission from the Isle of Wight. It was one of the first coastal wireless stations.

The circuits used at the Lizard and similar stations were very simple and, of course, included no 'active' devices (valves or tubes, transistors or integrated circuits). The transmitter was 'all electrical' and consisted of an accumulator power source which powered an induction coil when the key was closed. The output of the induction coil was connected to a spark gap of about 1cm. This was connected to the antenna via a tuned circuit.

The operation of the Lizard Wireless Station was taken over by the General Post Office in 1909. The first distress call handled by the Lizard was shortly before

Marconi plaque at the Lizard Wireless Station.
ALAN KITTRIDGE

EQUIPMENT AT THE LIZARD WIRELESS STATION

The primary source of oscillating energy came from the spark generated by the induction coil. Across the spark gap was the primary of the aerial transformer or 'jigger' and a series condenser (Leyden jar(s)) forming a tuned circuit. The secondary of the jigger was connected between the antenna and earth.

The receiver was also very simple; the receiving aerial and earth were connected via a tuned circuit to a detector. The output of the detector was originally connected *via* a relay to a morse-inker as used with land line telegraphy. Later, much greater sensitivity was found by using high impedance headphones. The earliest detector used was the coherer.

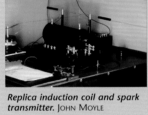

Replica induction coil and spark transmitter. JOHN MOYLE

The coherer was superceded by the magnetic detector or 'Maggie' which became the standard detector between 1908 and the introduction of vacuum valves (known as vacuum 'tubes' in the USA).

The induction coil and spark-gap are on the table at the extreme right with the Morse key in front. To the left of the clock is a coherer detector and to the left is a morse inker which marked the incoming Morse code on narrow paper tape.

The original equipment is shown in the upper photograph. The equipment at the Lizard Wireless Station today is a replica set, built in the workshops of The Telegraph Museum, Porthcurno for the National Trust.

The Lizard Wireless Station ALAN KITTRIDGE

midnight on 18 April 1910. The *Minnehaha* owned by The Atlantic Transport Company, ran aground off the Scillies. She was inbound from New York carrying passengers and cattle. The coastguards and Lloyds were alerted and she was quickly attended by tugs from Falmouth and refloated.

Operation at 1MHz with the call-sign 'GLD' commenced in 1913. In addition, in 1919, 667kHz was added using the callsign 'BVY'. In 1925, 375kHz was also added.

In 1913, the Lizard Station was moved to Land's End and became Land's End Radio using the famous callsign 'GLD'

The Lizard Wireless Station was restored by the National Trust who now own it. There is a room containing an amateur radio station to commemorate this historic site. The technical side of the site is maintained by volunteers, members of the Radio Officers Association.

THE COHERER

Before the invention of the first valve in 1904, very insensitive 'non-electronic' devices were used. The first practical detector of radio waves was the coherer. It consisted of a small glass tube containing some iron filings held loosely between two silver plugs. Under the influence of radio waves, the filings cohered so that they passed a current more easily. The current in turn operated a relay which actuated a Morse-inker spelling out the signal in terms of dots and dashes. An automatic 'tapper' 'de-cohered' the filings after the radio wave ceased. The coherer was sluggish and insensitive in use and required constant attention.

Coherer receiver MUSEUM OF SCIENCE, OXFORD.

In 1902 British ships and shore stations changed to the magnetic detector or 'Maggie' which was much more sensitive and stable and with syntonic (tuned) circuits made the receiver much more selective. The other advantage of the Maggie was that was that it produced an audible signal through headphones. Again functional description would be out of place here. The Maggie consisted of a moving band of iron wire passing around two pulleys, one of which was rotated by a clockwork motor. The band passed through two concentric coils, one connected to the antenna and the other to headphones. Over the coils were a pair of permanent magnets.

Maggie MUSEUM OF SCIENCE, OXFORD.

Poldhu wireless station. PK TRUST ARCHIVE

POLDHU WIRELESS STATION

Marconi chose Poldhu as it was in the west and therefore the shortest route to his goal of spanning the Atlantic but also because he considered that such a high power of electromagnetic emission may cause interference to power lines in close proximity in Chelmsford where his company was. Marconi's main target was to increase the range of wireless telegraphy. He had already found that range increased as the square of the height of the aerial and that radio signals would follow the curvature of the earth but aerial height was limited to around 200 feet. To increase the range, more power was required from the transmitter into the aerial. Until Poldhu, all Marconi's transmitters had been based on induction coils providing the spark energy. In 1899 he appointed Professor J. A. Fleming FRS of University College, London to develop a powerful 25 kilowatt transmitter which used an alternator and transformer to charge a huge bank of 'condensers' to a high voltage thus producing a very high energy spark discharge.

Poldhu wireless station staff 1907

It was said that the sound of the spark of the Poldhu transmitter could be heard a mile away!

The Poldhu Station was opened in January 1901 with the callsign 'ZZ'. In November, Marconi sailed for Newfoundland. When his receiving station there was ready, he cabled Poldhu on 9

December to instruct them to begin sending the prearranged signal 'SSS' at regular intervals from 3pm to 6pm daily. On Thursday 12 December 1901 he claimed that the 'SSS' signals had been received.

In February 1902, Marconi sailed from England towards the USA in the steamship *Philadelphia* to measure the range of the Poldhu transmitter. Using a morse inker he recorded the message at a range of up to 700 miles by day and up to 1,551 miles by night. 'SSS' was detectable at a range of 2,099 miles.

Marconi monument, Poldhu
ALAN KITTRIDGE

Poldhu continued as a high power maritime wireless station. In 1904 transmission began of Ocean News, a news bulletin which was reproduced for liner passengers. The callsign MPD at a frequency of 107kHz was used from 1913. During the Great War, Poldhu was used for occasional broadcasts to shipping although it was under the control of the War Office. Ocean News broadcasts resumed in 1919 and from 1920 regular weather forecasts were broadcast. In 1921, Poldhu was used to broadcast telegrams to ships which were out of range of the lower powered MF (medium frequency) coastal stations. In 1933, Poldhu Wireless Station finally closed. From then Portishead Wireless Station near Bristol became the UK's long distance radio station for communication with shipping.

A monument now stands on the Poldhu transmitter site. The Memorial column with its brass plates cost £356.16s.

The only remains of the Poldhu wireless station are some of the concrete bases of the aerial masts.

The Marconi archives (now housed at the Bodleian Library at Oxford University) show that in 1904 Marconi and his engineers were considering setting up another powerful wireless station at Goonhilly. However, there were problems with the site. There was uncertainty about the geology at Goonhilly. Also the topsoil was quite shallow and very boggy due to springs. The bogginess was made worse during the period from November to May by rain. Strong winds from January to mid April also limited construction time. It would have been possible to drain the land with pumps but this would have been very costly as there is no nearby river to pump into.

Cartage would also have been difficult and there was a scarcity of accommodation, which would have cost £250 per workman. From an electrical point of view, Goonhilly was considered to have 'bad earths'. For all these reasons Goonhilly was too expensive and so Marconi built the station in Ireland instead.

Poldhu today with the Marconi visitor centre on the right, housing a display and Poldhu Amatuer Radio Club
THORA KITTRIDGE

DIRECTION FINDING (DF) AND MULLION

During the Great War, Cornwall had important airship bases for patrolling the South Western approaches to hunt for German submarines. One air ship station was RNAS Mullion (SW 70 20) at Bonython, just north-east of Mullion village (the site is now a wind farm). Exact navigation was necessary and was especially difficult in poor weather. The greatest scientific advances are usually initiated by military conflict and the need to locate sources of radio transmission was of great strategic importance. The source of any radio transmission can be localised by using a receiver with a directional aerial. Aerials may be designed to be omni-directional, transmitting or receiving equally in all directions but by careful design aerials may also be made highly directional. Direction finding aerial-receiver combinations were optimised to find the bearing or azimuth of a transmitter but were unable, of course, to measure the distance. By taking bearings from two or preferably three sites the position of the transmitter can be located.

Position plotting by taking two bearings by direction finding

The Mullion DF Station was set up at Bonython (SW 69 21) and was later moved to Mile End, where the operators lived. All that can be seen now is their row of cottages, now privately owned. The Mullion Station in conjunction with another at Prawle Point in Devon enabled the position of the airships to be determined and radioed to their navigators. The call signs of the Mullion station were BVY and BVW during the Great War and it operated at a range of frequencies. At the end of the war RNAS Mullion was closed and all the buildings dismantled. The Admiralty realised the importance of DF and built a permanent DF station at Mile End. In 1924 it was transferred to the Post Office and provided a DF service until it closed in 1936.

DF equipment as used at Mile End and Bonython.
MUSEUM OF SCIENCE, OXFORD

GONIOMETER AND MARCONI DF RECEIVER

At sea and in the air, where space is limited, directional loop aerials are the norm at high frequency (HF). On land where space is not so much of a premium, early HF direction finding commonly used the Bellini-Tosi system first published in 1908. It consisted of two large vertical loops at right angles to each other. The feeds from these aerials were connected to a goniometer. The goniometer is a transformer with two primary windings or 'field coils' at right angles to each other. The secondary winding or 'rotatable search coil' is connected to the receiver. The rotational control is calibrated with the compass rose. Thus the secondary is rotated by hand until the received signal is either at a maximum or more commonly a minimum and thus the direction of the source of the signal is indicated.

MUSEUM OF SCIENCE, OXFORD

29

In the five years from 1896 the range of wireless transmission and reception increased dramatically from just over one mile to 2,000 miles. It became obvious that the most important use of this new technology was communication with ships at sea (and later aircraft) because of the impossibility of connection by wire. Not only was there the convenience of communication for commercial and social reasons but safety at sea improved dramatically.

From 1900 to the mid-1920s, only low frequencies of less than 1MHz were used; this would now be referred to as LF or low frequencies. This was before there was an understanding of ionosphere and the science of propagation.

Wireless (now more often known as 'radio') stations transmit at specific frequencies. Frequency is the number of cycles of radio energy per second, or c/s. A million cycles per second is abbreviated to 1Mc/s or in modern parlance, 1 Mega Hertz (1 MHz) after Heinrich Hertz (1857-1941), a German physicist who worked on electromagnetic radiation. The frequency of a wireless station may also be quoted as a wavelength. Because radio waves travel at the constant speed of light, a single cycle has a specific distance that it will travel dependent upon its frequency. The transmission and reception of radio waves is most efficient when the size of aerials used are certain fractions of the wavelength of the transmission. In the early days of wireless, wavelength was usually quoted as it related to the size of aerials and therefore wavelength was easier to measure than frequency. Today we would refer to frequency in terms of Hertz where 1Hz = 1c/s (cycle per second). So when discussing short wave marine communications, frequency therefore will be referred to as 'Megs' (megacycles per second) and kc/s (pronounced 'kay-sees' - kilo cycles per second).

Land's End Radio was a Coastal Radio Station of which there were 15 around the coast of the UK. The range of the Coastal Stations was of the order of a few hundred miles to a thousand miles at the most. There was one Long Range Maritime Radio Station in the UK and that was Portishead Radio in Somerset. With good conditions Portishead could be contacted from the other side of the world.

In the early days of wireless, low frequency, long wavelength and high power were considered to be the requisites of increasing the range of communication. It was not until the 1920s with greater understanding of radio wave propagation that the benefits of higher frequencies were understood. At higher frequencies it became apparent that radio signals were reflected by the 'ionosphere' and the sea so that long distances could be covered beyond the horizon.

Long distance radio wave propagation beyond the horizon relies on refraction and reflection from the ionosphere. The propagation angle varies with frequency and type of antenna.

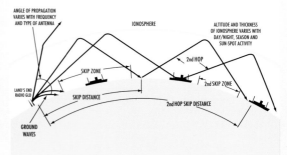

Rame signal station today. ALAN KITTRIDGE

RAME SIGNAL STATION

Rame Head has a long history as a nautical lookout post as it provides a good view of the approaches to Plymouth. The first indication of its use was during the Napolionic Wars in 1794. In 1890 the Great Western Railway and the local shipping agents set-up a signal station. Lloyds at some stage took-over the service and it was transferred to HM Coastguard in 1925 and Coastwatch in 1998. Nearby is the RDF transmitter for the Coastguard Centre at Brixham.

Rame signalman and committee 1927.
ALAN KITTRIDGE COLLECTION

LAND'S END RADIO – GLD

The move of the Lizard Wireless Station to St Just led to its being renamed. Land's End Radio was probably the most famous coastal radio station in the World communicating with shipping from 1913 (when it was built) following the closure of Lizard Radio. It maintained its fame and almost a romantic air as it was often the first contact with home after many months away. The initial move from the Lizard was to near the village of St Just in Penwith (SW 371309). To avoid interference, the radio operators with the sensitive receivers were separated from the transmitter by several miles. The transmitters were keyed remotely from the operator's desk.

Land's End radio station in the 1930s. BRIAN FAULKNER

There was a steady increase in the number of ships with radio fitted to improve safety and communication between ships and their owners. In 1928 GLD and other coast stations were equipped to exchange radiotelegrams and radiotelephony (R/T) was introduced but it was not until 1937 that ships were able to communicate direct with land line subscribers.

In 1939, with the beginning of Second World War, the Admiralty introduced censorship and all commercial traffic through GLD ceased for the duration. However, GLD was constantly manned by operators listening for transmissions from ships being attacked by the Germans. These transmissions from ships under attack were prefixed by SSSS (attack by submarine), AAAA (attack by aircraft), RRRR (attack by surface raider). GLD's role was then to report the attack with, if possible, the bearing and to help co-ordinate rescue if within range.

With the cessation of hostilities, GLD continued with a full and increasing commercial service but with a constant watch on the emergency frequencies which

Land's End radio station c.1937. BRIAN FAULKNER

always took precedence. Many famous rescues have been co-ordinated by GLD and the operators have been responsible for the saving of many thousands of lives.

The operating frequencies were 500kHz and 1MHz. In 1930, 2MHz was added and in 1951, 1.6MHz. VHF telephony was also added in 1959 using 156.8MHz Channel 16. Space at St Just was limited and therefore the receivers and operators moved to a new purpose-built home at Skewjack (SW 373249) near Sennen village in 1979 with the transmitters still remotely controlled at St Just (SW 378307). The building at Skewjack is still visible although now deserted and on private land.

In 1974, a VHF transceiver was installed at the Telegraph Tower in Scilly, remotely controlled from Skewjack but due to economies this was replaced by a transceiver with a directional aerial at GLD in 1986.

Land's End radio station, Skewjack. BRIAN FAULKNER   *Land's End radio station at Skewjack.* JOHN MOYLE

THE CLOCK

The life of the operator at Coastal Radio Stations was ruled by The Clock, which was in a prominent position. It was not just an ordinary clock but was set to keep GMT and had special markings on it. At the London Radio Conference in 1912 it was internationally agreed that there should be fixed silent periods which would be marked on the ships' radio room clocks during which no one would transmit and everyone would listen on 500kHz for distress signals. These times were marked in red. In 1947 at the Atlanta City Conference, similar periods were marked in green as silence periods for radiotelephony on 2182kHz.

THE DEMISE OF COASTAL RADIO STATIONS

The new millennium brought a close to a century of communication and above all safety provided by the services of radio stations like GLD. It also heralded a new era of communication and safety at sea by satellite communication.

Since the 1980s, GMDSS, Global Maritime Distress & Safety System, a modern and very complicated communications system for use at sea has led to the demise of the sea-going wireless operator or 'Sparks' and the coastal radio stations including GLD. Sparks has been replaced in larger vessels by an 'electronics' officer. Although this is a great advance in communications there are many who consider it both as a retrograde step in safety at sea and a cost cutting measure as there is no longer a need for a 24 hour watch either at sea or on land. Wireless telegraphy with basic, robust, equipment using Morse code was incredibly reliable and should have been maintained as a back up for safety. GMDSS, will only save life if all the following are working at the time of distress at sea:

- Ship-borne computer
- Ship-borne satellite communication system and its dish which may not be able to be directed at the satellite if the ship is listing.
- Satellite
- Land-based satellite communication system
- Land-based Computer system
- Land-line communications

There are also possibilities of the system failing in time of war or malicious jamming of the satellite. All of the world's major 500kHz wireless telegraphy stations have been closed leaving no reliable and simple back-up to a highly complex system. Morse code, simple robust radio equipment and a wire aerial are incredibly reliable in comparison to the sophisticated GMDSS system which provides fantastic communication facilities in good weather and peacetime but there have already been a number of reports of failure in foul weather due to damage to ship-borne satellite dishes.

The last transmission from Land's End Radio was on 31 December 1997 and it signalled the end of a century of wireless telegraphy at sea.

Land's End radio station in the 1950s. Brian Faulkner

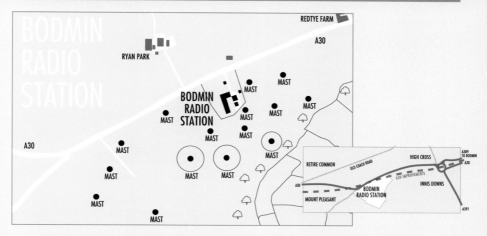

Bodmin Beam Wireless Station (SX 018627) near Lanivet village, must have been an impressive sight. The location was selected with great care not only from a technical point of view but well inland to reduce the possibility of bombardment by hostile navies. In the early 20th century, the UK Government with the agreement of the Governments of Canada, South Africa, Australia and India planned to set up an Imperial Wireless Chain instead of using cables. Most of the buildings have now been demolished to make way for the new A30 dual carriageway. The cost of setting up a long distance wireless station was approximately a tenth of that of submarine cables. In order to facilitate reliable wireless communication over such distances, aerial systems known as 'beam aerials' were used. The Franklin Beam aerials at the wavelengths used in the Imperial Wireless Chain were vast. They consisted of a 'radiator' with a 'reflector' behind. They were supported by 300ft masts with 90ft cross spars making them 'T'-shaped. The masts were in a row 1,200ft in length. The Bodmin aerials were directed towards Canada and South Africa.

The first service was to Canada on a frequency of 11.5 MHz and commenced on 25 October 1926. A second service to South Africa started the following year on 5 July.

In view of the enormous power of the transmitter, the receiver was geographically at some distance, at Bridgwater in Somerset, to avoid interference from the transmitter.

The first transmissions from Bodmin were made in October 1926 using high speed Morse code at around 1,250 characters per minute. The beam transmissions ceased in 1939 and the equipment was moved to the Beam Station at Dorchester. The Bodmin Station was taken over by the RAF who erected omni-directional aerials for long range communication with aircraft.

In 1947, Cable & Wireless Ltd were asked to re-open Bodmin Radio for the Admiralty. Then in 1949 Bodmin Radio was handed back to the Post Office. During the 1950s the sign at the gate read 'Diplomatic Wireless Service'. Latterly it was in Naval use again for communication with submarines worldwide before finally closing in 2002.

THE SECOND WORLD WAR AND RADIO NAVIGATION

The Second World War was the first major conflict in which electronics had such a major effect upon the outcome. During the Great War, land-line telegraphy and telephony were important forms of communication. Much had to be learnt about security, codes and ciphers as even land-lines are susceptible to eavesdropping. Radio or 'wireless' (as it was then more usually referred to) was mainly used at sea, as systems in the early 20th century were not very portable. Security with wireless telegraphy was even more important

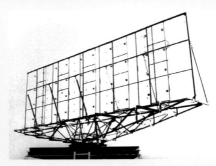

Chain Home Low radar antenna. JOHN LANGFORD

than with land-lines, not just for the security of information passed but also for the susceptibility to direction finding. Using directional aerials and taking bearings on a transmitting source from two or more receivers, it is possible to 'triangulate' and determine the position of a 'target' with considerable accuracy.

Just prior to the Second World War scientists on both sides of the conflict developed what we now know as radar. Radio waves travel at the speed of light. A pulsed radio emission is transmitted in a particular direction. It is reflected from metallic or other solid objects, be it a ship or an aeroplane, back to a receiver adjacent to the transmitter. Direction finding techniques pin-point the bearing or 'azimuth' of the target and by measuring the time taken for the pulse to travel to the target and back, the distance is measured.

The only remains of Second World War radar are the concrete bases of many of the antenna systems and a few block houses which are either in a bad state of disrepair or are being used for agricultural purposes.

SITES OF SECOND WORLD WAR RADAR STATIONS

Dunderhole Point	SX 047880
Trevose Head	SW 852764
Trerew	SW 815585
St Agnes Beacon	SW 705505
Marks Castle West Penwith	SW 345250
Carn Brea	SW 386281
Sennen	SW 376246
Pen Olver	SW 712121
Dry Tree (Goonhilly)	SW 725212
Treleaver	SW 775165
Trelanvean	SW 751196
Jacka	SW 935395
Chapel Rame	SX 416438
Rame Head	SW 418483
Newford Down, Isles of Scilly	SV 913123

Chain Home Transmitter antenna masts, Trerew. AIR DEFENCE RADAR MUSEUM

The earliest radar, originally known as RDF for secrecy, was the Chain Home system. This consisted of 20 stations. Initially the most vulnerable south-east coast of England was protected but by the end of the war the whole the UK was protected. As Cornwall is the most south-westerly part of the UK, it was an important area for the installation of radar for protection from the enemy approaching from the sea or air.

RAF Trerew Chain Home Radar receiver building.
NICK CATFORD

Chain Home radar was the first strategically practical operational radar system in the world. It was a step in the evolution from direction finding to modern radar. Unlike later systems with recognisable rotation aerials or aerial, CH consisted of a large lattice transmitting aerial suspended between 300ft masts which 'flood-lit' a wide area with pulsed radio energy. Reception was by a direction-finding aerial and receiver. The information was displayed on a screen as a horizontal line calibrated with range in nautical miles from left to right. The bearing or 'azimuth' of the reflected returns was measured with a conventional direction finding system and the distance of the target measured by the delay of the return. The operator had to continuously alter the bearing of the receiver to search for 'returns' from targets; this required a lot of continuous attention. The search of a given area was carried out manually by the operator adjusting the goniometer bearing.

All future radar systems including Chain Home Low were based on a rotating antenna transmitting a narrow beam or pulsed radio waves. The same antenna receives the reflected signal. The result is displayed on the well-known Plan Position Indicator in a map-like fashion.

Gee Navigational ground stations, Master or Slave, were developed when the RAF realised that finding a target in the dark or poor weather conditions was far less accurate than had been claimed. It was the first radio-navigation system, which did not rely on direction finding. The SW Chain of Gee had a station at Sharpitor as the Master with 'slave' stations at Sennen and another in Dorset at Worth Matravers near Swanage. In 1944 a second generation of hyperbolic navigation was developed by the Decca Company. It was called the Decca Navigator (of which more later) and prototypes were used at the D-Day Landings at Normandy.

Chain Home and Chain Home Low were the first defence against incoming enemy aircraft. Each CH and CHL station was in contact with a Filter Station which in the case of the Cornish stations was the Western

Bass Point and Pen Olver radar 1944
SHAUN CHURCHILL

Filter Station near Box, Bath. Here the information from each station was analysed and compared. When enemy aircraft were sighted, the sector controller would 'scramble' fighter aircraft to intercept. The fighters were then directed to intercept by controllers at the GCI radar stations whose radar systems were of higher definition but shorter range. Whereas the CH, CHL and the sector controllers communicated with the squadrons, the GCI radar operators were in direct contact with the individual fighter pilots by radio telephone.

RSS AND THE Y SERVICE

SIGINT is the acronym for signals intelligence. In the Great War, but to a much greater extent in the Second World War, both sides of the conflict soon realised the value of listening to and analysing the enemy's radio communications. Intelligence could be gained, not only by decoding the actual messages, but by direction-finding the location of the source could be determined. Most radio operators engaged in this form of intelligence were volunteers and ex-radio amateurs. They formed part of the RSS or Radio Security Service known as the Y-Service. The brief of the RSS was to 'intercept, locate and close down illicit wireless stations operated either by enemy agents in Great Britain or by other persons not being licensed to do so under the Defence Regulations, 1939'. The radio operators were known as VIs or Voluntary Interceptors. The RSS was given the designation MI8c. Most VIs worked from home in a clandestine fashion and although their brief was originally to locate and monitor illicit signals from the UK, their main function became that of recording encrypted enemy signals and passing them to GCHQ. The RSS set up a number of direction finding stations around the UK. An important direction-finding site in the Second World War was at St Erth. The exact site of the station is not known but was probably on the highest open ground in the area. Most of the station was buried

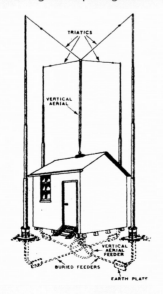

underground. The St Erth Station was set up by a Major Keen who was a DF expert at the Marconi Company. It had 17 receivers on different frequencies; two of these receivers were used for DF. The receivers and the VIs were in a metal walled room underground so as to avoid as much outside radio interference as possible. There were four vertical DF aerials in a 30 foot square. The St Erth DF station was set up and run by the RSS, the General Post Office and the Foreign Office. These organizations set up similar stations at St Just-in-Penwith (SW 3631) and Leedstown (SW 6034) but the exact sites are unknown. The Army also had a DF intercept station at Chacewater (SW 7544).

Direction finding antennas at St Erth. Four vertical antennas connected to a goniometer and receiver in the wooden hut.

The Decca Navigator system was a second generation hyperbolic navigation system. It became very popular soon after Second World War both at sea and in the air for its great accuracy. Later versions even automatically plotted the vessel's course directly onto a chart. Decca Navigator 'chains' of four synchronized transmitters covered most commonly used sea routes within 100 miles of land. The transmitters were located at Bolberry Down, Devon, St Helier, Jersey, St.Mary's, Isles of Scilly and Llancarfan, Wales, and provided coverage for the south and south east coasts of Ireland, Cornwall and the Scilly Isles. It began operation in 1952 and was finally closed in 2000.

DeccaNavigator position display for marine use. Readings from the meters were transposed to special marine charts giving position with great accuracy.

Hyperfix was another hyperbolic navigation system developed by Decca in the 1960s. It was used on a much smaller scale than the Decca Navigator but was extremely accurate and used mainly by the off-shore oil and gas industry. In the year 2000, the UK Ministry of Defence decommissioned the Hyperfix stations that were located around the British Coast. One of these was the station located at Bass Point, Lizard, Cornwall. The site lies on land formerly occupied by RAF Pen Olver, a Second World War CHL radar station, and there are derelict RAF buildings scattered around. All of the hyperbolic navigation systems were victims of the GPS (Global Positioning System) satellite system and have now closed.

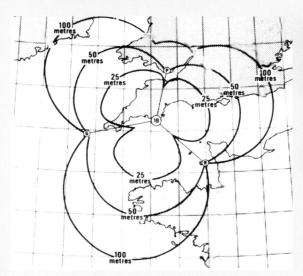

Decca Navigator slave tramsmitter.
PK ARCHIVES

Range and accuracy of SW Decca Navigator chain. The Green (G) transmitter was on St Mary's on the Isles of Scilly. 49.933 N, 6.300 W. SV 915125.

MORWENSTOW

The Radio Station at Morwenstow (SS 204126), near Bude, is an outpost of GCHQ, the Government Communications Headquarters, what was known as the Composite Signals Organisation (CSO). It is on the site of RAF Cleave which closed as an RAF station in November 1945. The Ministry of Defence still owned the land until it was transferred to the Ministry of Public Buildings and Works in 1967 in preparation for the building of CSO Morwenstow which began in 1969. CSO Morwenstow was completed in 1972 and became fully operational in 1974. The term CSO dates from the bringing together of the civilian intercept organizations of GCHQ, the Admiralty, the War Office and the Air Ministry in 1964. In July 2001, the site was renamed GCHQ Bude where approximately 200 people work, living within the local community. 'Spy' satellites listen in to any radio emissions of interest and the receiving dishes at stations like GCHQ Bude then pass the information to computers using the ECHELON system. ECHELON which has a US Patent No. 5418951 is a system with a global network of computers that automatically search through millions of intercepted messages for pre-programmed keywords or fax, telex and e-mail addresses. Every word of every message in the frequencies and channels selected at a station is automatically searched. The processors in the network are known as the ECHELON Dictionaries. The dictionaries contain thousands of words such as 'explosives',' bombs', 'armament', 'kill', 'president', 'prime minister' and the names of all the heads of State and other senior government personnel. If one of the dictionary words is included in a message then that message is recorded for analysis but otherwise it is rejected.

Earlier radio spying had to be done by receiving stations at ground level but these could not listen to distant UHF or VHF transmissions as they travel only line of sight and not over the horizon. So much communication today is digital, (for example text messages and emails) and most of it is wireless that there is a wealth of information in the ether to spy upon. Much of this communication is at such high frequencies that it can only travel by line of sight over short distances at ground level but very long distances upwards where it can be received by spy satellites. These communications are then retransmitted and received by stations such as that at Bude. The vast majority of intercepted messages are of no use for intelligence but ECHELON sifts the 'wheat from the chaff'.

Morwenstow and the other similar UK and USA sites may have reached the peak of the intercept ability. Communications via undersea telegraphy cables were difficult but not impossible to intercept without the sender and recipient realising that security had been breached. Cables were tapped and even diverted but it was no easy feat without detection. Radio communications are inherently insecure and it is only by the use of codes and ciphers that any security is possible. The use of satellites and ground-stations make communication of huge numbers of channels possible beyond the horizon. It is no coincidence that Morwenstow was set-up just a short distance from the world's largest 'Earth Station' at Goonhilly. It is also no coincidence that the dishes at Morwenstow are trained in the same direction as those at Goonhilly.

However, satellite communication has an inherently high capital and running cost. The new fibre-optic cable technology is much cheaper and a single cable can carry at least 100 times more channels of communication than a single satellite. Unfortunately for GCHQ it is impossible at present to intercept communications via submarine fibre-optic cables. The GCHQ site at Morwenstow is very obvious but in this day and age it would be unwise to approach too close to the site.

British Telecom suddenly announced in September 2006 that the Goonhilly Earth Station would be closed in 2008. Goonhilly was once rejected by Marconi as the site for another wireless station in the early 20th century because the ground was too boggy but now the location is known the world over as one of the first and still the largest "Earth Station" for satellite communications.

Workers at the completion of ARTHUR. BT

Goonhilly Satellite Earth Station was opened by the Post Office, as BT was then known as, in 1962 along with Pleumeur Bodou in France and Andover in the USA as the first of about 200 similar stations operating now.

It was originally built to take part in the Telstar and Relay projects to determine the feasibility of satellite communications. The Telstar project which was launched by NASA and AT&T was the one that captured the public interest as it was the first time television signals were transmitted across the Atlantic. The ultra-high frequencies required to transmit TV images only propagate in straight lines and do not follow the curvature of the earth; the maximum range of TV transmissions is the horizon. Telstar was the first satellite put into orbit with the main purpose of intercontinental TV. The site at Goonhilly was chosen because it was in the west of the UK (shortest distance) and because the Lizard is a reasonably flat plateau with no higher ground for many miles. This means that a steerable dish antenna can be directed to a satellite which may be very low on the horizon in any direction without interference. Amazingly, Aerial No 1 also know as *Arthur* was conceived, designed and erected in just 12 months to be ready for the launch of Telstar. There is a story that the communication workers union called a national strike of all Post Office staff during this critical period but that work continued at Goonhilly because "it was in Cornwall, not England"!

Control room in 1962 during the first contact with TELSTAR. BT

On the 11th July 1962 at 02.44 hours precisely, the first TV images were beamed down to Goonhilly from the USA via Telstar. In 1962, a second giant dish was designed and built by the Marconi Company. By the year 2000, the 160 acre site had 61 satellite dishes of all sizes.

Goonhilly handled commercial communication traffic to and from the countries surrounding the Atlantic and Indian Oceans. The traffic was in the form of telephone calls, data, fax, and telex and television. It never handled military communications. The transmitters and receivers associated with the dishes were directed at satellites in geostationary orbits allowing communication at great distances over the horizon as shown in the diagram.

Over the years the site expanded and developed to meet international telecommunications expectations and in its peak handled millions of international phone, fax, video, TV and data signals.

SATELLITE

| PROPULSION SYSTEM |
| TELEMETRY, ATTITUDE CONTROL COMMANDING, FUEL, BATTERIES POWER, THERMAL SYSTEMS |

SOLAR PANELS — SOLAR PANELS

| DOWNCONVERTER PRE-AMPLIFIER FILTER | HIGH POWER AMPLIFIER FILTER |
| RECEIVER SECTION | TRANSMITTER SECTION |

UPLINK DOWNLINK

EARTH STATIONS / ANTENNAS

The site has also dealt with a variety of ship to shore, aeroplane to land and more specialist services via fibre optic cables. The antennas themselves are still extremely impressive, with the largest dish currently on site possessing a dish diameter of 32 metres and weighing in at 1100 tonnes, which creates quite an impact on the local landscape.

The proportion of international communication *via* satellites has actually fallen over the last few decades although the work of Goonhilly had increased. The reason for this is that as communication is increasing exponentially, it is more economical to revert to submarine cables once again for the shorter distances to Europe, Scandinavia and even North Africa. The difference between the submarine cables of the early 20th century and those now being used is that optical fibres have replaced electrical conductors. Optical fibre cables are more reliable and economical than their electrical counterpart and are able to carry many more 'circuits' ('channels') and at higher speeds and require far fewer 'repeaters'.

The No 1 dish, *Arthur*, has not been in used for some years but is a Grade II Listed building and therefore will remain maintained after BT close the rest of the site.

Goonhilly control room. BT

The site has a fascinating visitor centre and it is assumed that the Goonhilly Earth Station will remain open as a historic communication site for many years to come.

In 2006, BT decided for operational reasons to consolidate all of its satellite services to Goonhilly's sister station at Madley in Herefordshire. In effect this means that all satellite dishes at Goonhilly could be decommissioned and most probably dismantled bar the original dish, *Arthur*.

Despite the loss of satellite services, Goonhilly will continue as an operational site with Research & Development and other communications services for many years to come, including Fibre Optic Cables.

From 2008 and 2010 a visitor centre was open, with many exhibits, one of the fastest cybercafes and tours around the site and Arthur. Despite attracting some 80,000 visitors BT closed it in 2010. In 2011 the site was leased to Goonhilly Earth Station Ltd whose intention is to develop a space science centre specialising in radio astronomy, satellite control and satellite communications services. A new visitor centre is planned but no opening date is available at the time of writing.

Goonhilly Earth Station. ALAN KITTRIDGE

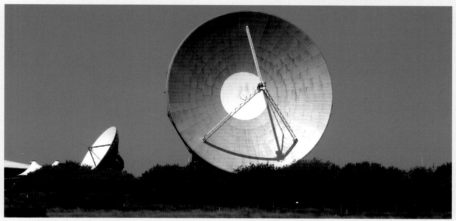

SATELITE NAVIGATION

Global Navigation Satellite Systems include the well-known GPS (Global Positioning System) and GLONAS, a Russian satellite based system. DGNSS or Differential GNSS is a method of locally improving the accuracy of satellite navigation by the use of special radio beacons which use the old radio-navigational beacon frequencies. Of the 14 DGNSS beacons around the UK coast, there is one on the Lizard Peninsula (SW 704115).

It first came into operation in 1998 and transmits at 306kHz. It has a range of around 250 nautical miles. All large ships have satellite navigation equipment that automatically combines the signals from the satellites with that from the nearest DGNSS station to improve the accuracy of navigation.

PLACES TO VISIT

Many of the sites mentioned in this guide can be viewed or entered from a public way. However, the inclusion of any site does not necessarily mean there is a right of access and when in doubt it is advisable and courteous to seek permission from the owner. Details of museums or attractions open to the public are given here but, as many are seasonal, it is always wise to check opening dates and times before travelling a distance.

THE LIZARD

RNAS CULDROSE
(SW 670253) is the largest helicopter station in Europe and has a large primary and secondary radar system which is the most obvious landmark on entering the Lizard peninsula. There is a visitor centre.

GOONHILLY SATELLITE EARTH STATION (SW 724213)
Sadly BT announced the closure of this major site as a functioning satellite

earth station from 2008, but the largest of the dishes, Arthur, which is a Grade II listed structure, will remain. An enhanced visitor attraction opened but closed in 2010. Since then the site has been leased to a new company to develop as a space science centre. It is hoped to have a visitor centre again in due course but no firm details are currently available.

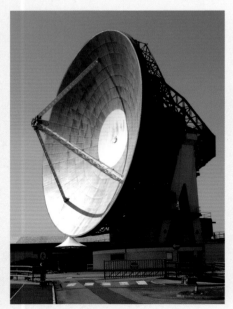

ARTHUR at Goonhilly ALAN KITTRIDGE

DRY TREE RADAR STATION
(SW 727210)
Evidence in concrete and brick of RAF Dry Tree Radar Station lies to the SE of Goonhilly Earth Satellite Station adjacent to the B3293 road – now a nature reserve.

LLOYDS SIGNAL STATION
(SW 714119)
Lloyds Signal Station at Bass Point is now privately occupied as a residence but externally looks as it did when operational initially as a visual-only signal station but soon connected to shipping agents in Falmouth by land-line telegraph

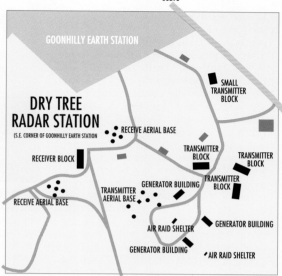

B3293

GOONHILLY EARTH STATION

DRY TREE
RADAR STATION
(S.E. CORNER OF GOONHILLY EARTH STATION)

SMALL TRANSMITTER BLOCK

RECEIVE AERIAL BASE

RECEIVER BLOCK

TRANSMITTER BLOCK

TRANSMITTER BLOCK

TRANSMITTER BLOCK

GENERATOR BUILDING

TRANSMITTER AERIAL BASE

RECEIVE AERIAL BASE

AIR RAID SHELTER

GENERATOR BUILDING

GENERATOR BUILDING

AIR RAID SHELTER

There is a **COASTWATCH LOOKOUT STATION** on the cliff edge adjacent to the Lloyds Signal Station. Visitors are welcome.

And the ruins of **PEN OLVER RADAR STATION (**SW 713120) are nearby.

Coastwatch Station at Bass Point ALAN KITTRIDGE

Pen Olver Radar Station. JOHN MOYLE

LIZARD WIRELESS STATION

(SW 711119)

Telephone 01326 290384 for a recorded message about opening times or the National Trust office 01326 561407. The station is located just over half a mile from the Lizard village. By its very nature and location it is not wheelchair friendly. The walk from the lighthouse gives the visitor truly spectacular views but requires a degree of fitness as there is a steep decent and climb to the Housel Bay beach to be navigated, and therefore, should only be attempted by able people. The walk down Lloyds Lane (no vehicular traffic) is relatively flat, or you can walk to the Housel Bay Hotel and have lunch or tea at the Hotel before visiting the station. Access is by foot only and it can be reached from the Lizard village car park. Follow the signs to the Housel Bay Hotel. A path runs adjacent to the hotel

Lizard Lighthouse. Alan Kittridge

out onto the cliff; turn left and follow the path along the cliff top for a few minutes until the wireless station is reached. The more active can drive to the National Trust car park at the Lizard lighthouse and walk east for about a mile taking in the spectacular views and joining the path at the Housel Bay Hotel. (www.lizardwireless.org)

Inside Lizard Wireless Station today. Alan Kittridge

Poldhu Cove with the site of Poldhu Hotel and Poldhu Wireless Station on the right. GORDON HILL

LIZARD LIGHTHOUSE

(SW 704115) with foghorn, navigational radio beacon and DGPS transmitter. There is also a museum of Trinity House and Lighthouse equipment. Telephone 01326 290202 or email lighthouselizard@aol.com for opening times. A visit to the museum includes a guided tour of the working lighthouse. There is a National Trust car park next to the lighthouse and the most southery cafe in England nearby.

HOUSEL BAY HOTEL

(SW 707121)
This was Marconi's second home whilst working at the Lizard wireless station and at Poldhu.

KENNACK SANDS

(SW 734165) There is a cable hut which still exists 200 metres beyond the end of the tarmac road going east from the village of Kuggar SW 724163. The cable hut is shown on 2nd edition Ordnance Survey maps of 1907 but which submarine cables lead from the hut are open to question.

The Marconi Centre, Poldhu. ALAN KITTRIDGE

MARCONI CENTRE

(SW 663196)
The Marconi Centre is a joint project between The National Trust, Marconi plc and Poldhu Amateur Radio Club. It commemorates the Poldhu Wireless Station the only remains of which are the concrete bases of the aerial masts. There is a monument. The Amateur Radio Club building houses a display of the history of Marconi at Poldhu. Licensed radio amateurs may operate from the clubhouse radio station. Telephone 01326 241656 (Post code TR12 7JB) www.gb2gm.org.uk. Parking is at the pay and display car park at SW 667195. Do not drive up the obvious steep hill to the site as this is a private road with no parking on it, to the home for the elderly which was once the Poldhu Hotel.

LAND'S END RADIO

The original building at St Just (SW 378307) is now privately owned but can be seen from the road. The site at Skewjack Farm (SW 365249) near Sennen village, to where Land's End Radio moved in 1979, is also now on private land but visible from the road adjacent to an ugly modern building owned by British Telecom.

CARN BREA (SW 386281)

Carn Brea has a fantastic panoramic view and was the site of the semaphore telegraph communicating with the Isles of Scilly. There is no evidence of the radar beacon visible now

PORTHCURNO

TELEGRAPH MUSEUM (SW 384227)

An essential place to visit. The PK Trust's two major activities are operation of the award-winning Porthcurno Telegraph Museum and the management of the

CAPE CORNWALL

ST JUST
A3071

LAND'S END RADIO GLD
ST JUST 1913-1979

LAND'S END RADIO GLD
ST JUST TRANSMITTERS 1913-2000

B3306

CHAPEL CARN BREA
FIRE BEACON SITE
SEMAPHORE TO ISLES OF SCILLY
SECOND WORLD WAR RADAR BEACON

WHITESAND BAY
CABLES TO IRELAND
AND NORTH AMERICA

A30

CABLE HUT RUINS

SENNEN

GLD RECEIVING ANTENNA
1979-2000

LAND'S END

LAND'S END

MARKS CASTLE
CHAIN HOME RADAR STATION

SKEWJACK
LAND'S END RADIO GLD
MAIN STATION 1979-2000

B3283

TREEN

ZAWN REETH
TELEGRAPH CABLES TO
ISLES OF SCILLY
1869 AND 1879

TELEGRAPH MUSEUM

PENBERTH

PORTHCURNO

PQ
PYRAMID

HUER'S
HUT

CABLES ALL OVER
THE WORLD

Land's End Radio building, St Just. John Moyle

Porthcurno beach with the open-air Minack Theatre to the left. GORDON HILL

Cable & Wireless historic archive, developing Porthcurno's reputation as an important centre for the study of the history of communications. The main building houses displays of the history of submarine telegraphy from geographical, economic and social points of view. The tunnels contain displays and demonstrations of the technology from the first days of cable telegraphy through to the fibre optic cables of today.

From the end of March to October, the Museum is open daily, and during the winter months it is open on Sundays, Mondays and at other times by appointment.

For further information on visits telephone 01736 810966.

www.porthcurno.org.uk.

Entrance to the tunnels at Porthcurno. JOHN MOYLE

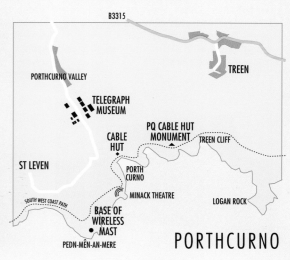

B3315

PORTHCURNO VALLEY

TREEN

TELEGRAPH MUSEUM

CABLE HUT

PQ CABLE HUT MONUMENT

TREEN CLIFF

ST LEVEN

PORTH CURNO

SOUTH WEST COAST PATH

MINACK THEATRE

LOGAN ROCK

BASE OF WIRELESS MAST

PEDN-MÊN-AN-MERE

PORTHCURNO

PQ cable hut marker, Treen Cliff, near Porthcurno. PK TRUST ARCHIVE

PQ CABLE HUT MARKER
(SW 390223)
A White Pyramid stands alongside the footpath between Porthcurno and Logan's Rock. It marks the site of a cable hut for the 1880 Brest to Cornwall cable. The hut was demolished which caused a furore amonst the fishermen who used it as a land mark so it was replaced by the pyramid.

ST ERTH
Sites of secret radio listening station, direction finding station and a radar station were on the hill (SW 562350) above the village close to the St Erth Hill which then become Steppy Down Road leading to St Erth Praze. At 79 metres above sea level this must have been a 'good wireless site' but there is no evidence left of what were mainly wooden buildings.

PQ cable hut on Treen Cliff. PK TRUST ARCHIVE